Mega English
Age 3–5

EGMONT
We bring stories to life

First published in Great Britain in 2004 by Egmont UK Limited
239 Kensington High Street, London W8 6SA
Published in this edition in 2009
© 2009 Egmont UK Limited

Activities by Brenda Apsley and Nina Filipek
Cover illustration by Craig Cameron, interior illustrations by John Haslam

ISBN 978 1 4052 4485 5
1 3 5 7 9 10 8 6 4 2
Printed in Italy

2 Contents

Contents

Mega Reading and Writing 3–5 offers lots of practice in literacy skills as described in the Curriculum Guidance for the Foundation Stage. The book's content is in line with the recommendations of the National Curriculum for England and Wales and the National Guidelines for Scotland.

This book is divided into five main sections:
- **preparation for reading;**
- **identifying letter sounds (phonics);**
- **preparation for writing;**
- **reading simple words;**
- **writing the letters.**

Within these sections children will learn to:
1. **observe details in pictures;**
2. **scan the page from left to right;**
3. **say the sounds of the letters;**
4. **match sounds to pictures;**
5. **tell a simple story;**
6. **use a pencil confidently;**
7. **form the letters of the alphabet.**

The book is aimed at children aged 3 to 5, so the levels of the exercises are progressively more difficult. The content begins at Nursery level and moves up to Reception level. We recommend that your child works through the book in the given order. If he or she starts to struggle or gets bored with any of the pages, skip these activities and return to them on another day when your child is feeling more positive and responsive. Repetition and practice will help build skills and confidence.

Your child can add the 100 fun stickers to the pages of the book as rewards for his or her efforts or use them to decorate pencil cases, posters or other items.

Checklist to record your child's achievements.

How to... pages contain useful parent notes.

How to help your child

Choose a time when your child is alert and eager to learn. Read aloud and point to the instructions on each page. These are written using a simple vocabulary for the age group, but you may also need to explain more fully what your child is being asked to do. Make sure your child can hold a pencil correctly and let your child decide how long he or she wants to work on the book. Always give lots of encouragement and praise for effort and enjoy the book together.

- **make time for reading stories to your child;**
- **show your child that you read yourself;**
- **enjoy sharing songs and rhymes;**
- **show your child that reading is fun.**

In preparation for reading, children need to learn to observe details: firstly, details in pictures and, later, details in words.

In this section, we will be developing observation skills by:

- **identifying pictures that are the same and pictures that are different;**
- **finding smaller pictures within larger pictures;**
- **telling a story based on pictures.**

Join the pictures that are the same.

Ring the odd one out in each row.

Tell a story about the pictures.

Ring the matching shadows.

Spot the differences in the pictures.

Ring the things you can find in the big picture.

What can't you see in the picture?

Spot the differences in the pictures.

Finish the pictures on the right.

Tell a story about the pictures.

Join the big shapes to the little shapes.

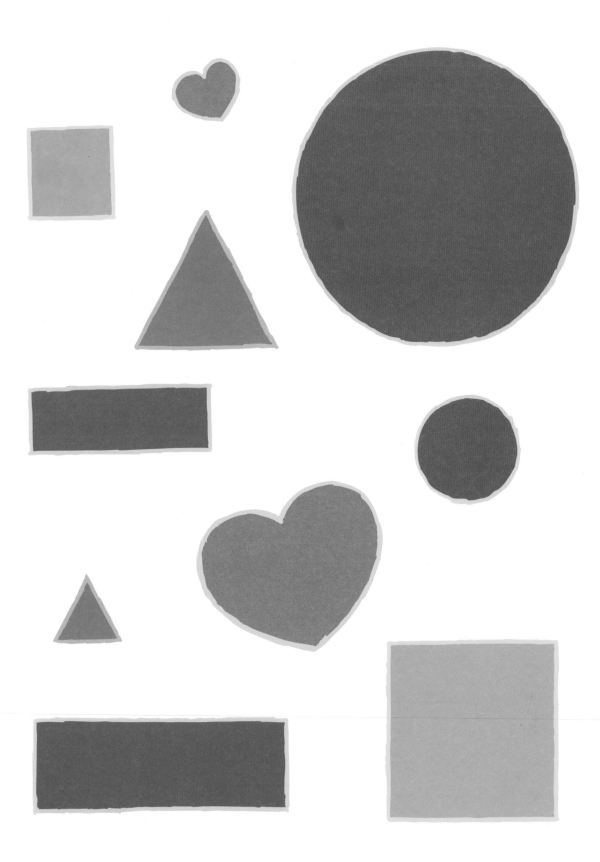

Join the things that go together.

Words are made up of letters that have corresponding sounds. Children need to learn the sounds of the letters to help them read or 'decode' words. This is what teachers call 'phonics'.

The sound of the letter is not the same as its name, for example, the sound of **b** is 'buh' but its name is 'bee'.

Here are the single letter sounds you should start with. Pronounce the letter sounds as they appear in the examples below.

a as in apple (hard sound)
not as in angel (soft sound)

b as in bed

c as in cup
not as in circle

d as in dog

e as in egg
not as in eagle

f as in fish

g as in gate
not as in giraffe

h as in hen

i as in igloo or insect
not as in ice

j as in jug

k as in kite or kitten

l as in leaf

m as in moon or mum

n as in nest

o as in orange
not as in oval

p as in pen or penguin

q as in queen

r as in ring

s as in sun

t as in tap

u as in umbrella
not as in unicorn

v as in vase

w as in window

x as in box not as
in xylophone

y as in yellow or yo-yo

z as in zip or zebra

Later on, when your child is ready, you can point out
that sometimes the same letter can
have different sounds.

Do you know the sounds of all the letters?
Point to the sound that begins your name.

a b c d e

f g h i j k

l m n o p q

r s t u v w

x y z

Ring the things that you can find in the big picture.

What can't you see in the picture?

Ring the odd one out in each row.

b   d   b   b   b   b

c   d   c   c   c   c

s   s   s   s   x   s

a   o   o   o   o   o

t   f   f   f   f   f

Join the letters that are the same.

Match the pictures to the sounds.

Match the pictures to the sounds.

Match the pictures to the sounds.

l

k

i

j

Match the pictures to the sounds.

p

m

n

o

Match the pictures to the sounds.

q

t

s

r

Match the pictures to the sounds.

 v

 w

u

Match the pictures to the sounds.

x

z

y

Tell a story about the pictures.

Ring the odd one out in each row.

j   j   j   q   j   j

k   k   k   k   k   z

p   y   p   p   p   p

r   r   r   r   u   r

w   v   v   v   v   v

Ring the sounds that match the pictures.

e   c

f   h

t   d

w   s

Ring the sounds that match the pictures.

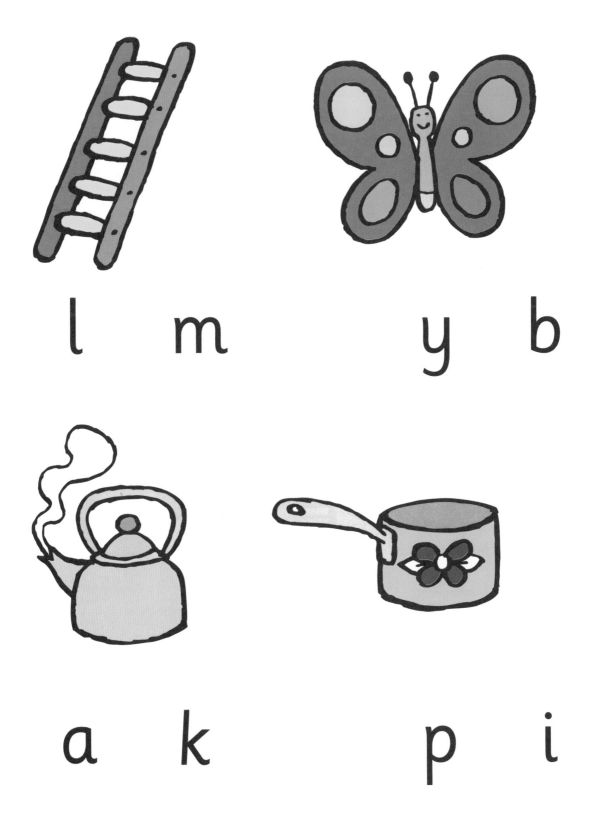

l   m   y   b

a   k   p   i

Ring the sounds that match the pictures.

r   q

w   u

v   z   g

o   x   n

Tell a story about the pictures.

- show your child your own writing, e.g. a list, or a message in a birthday card;
- encourage your child's 'pretend' writing;
- show your child that writing is fun.

In this section we will be developing pencil control skills by:

- drawing straight lines from left to right, and up and down;
- drawing circles in an anti-clockwise direction (in preparation for writing the letters o, a, e);
- drawing a variety of different lines, e.g. curved and zig-zag lines to encourage hand/eye co-ordination and fluent strokes.

Let's go!

Draw the lines for the snails to follow.

Finish the ladders for the dogs to climb.

Draw left to right

Show how the dolphins jump the waves.

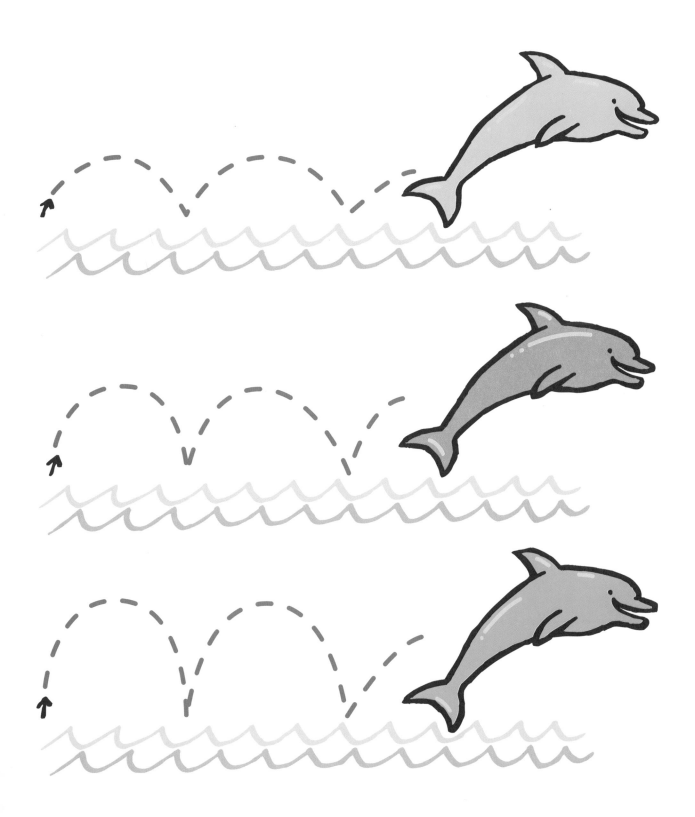

Draw lines to finish the bricks on Humpty Dumpty's wall.

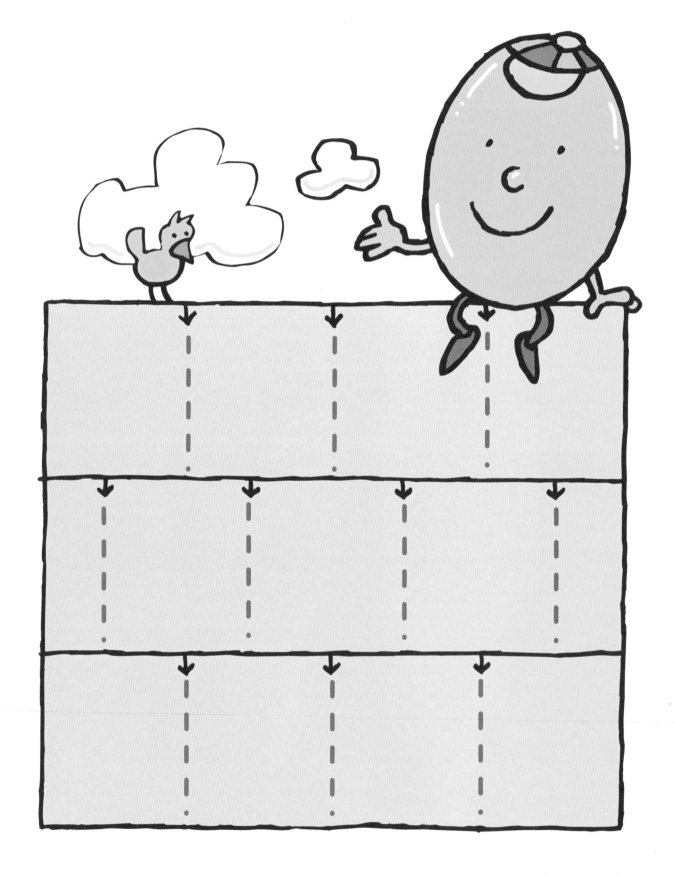

Show the mouse the way to his hole without touching the cat!

Draw lines to finish the pattern on the rug.

Finish drawing the woolly lambs.

Draw drips of water falling from the watering can.

Draw a line to take the spaceship to the planet.

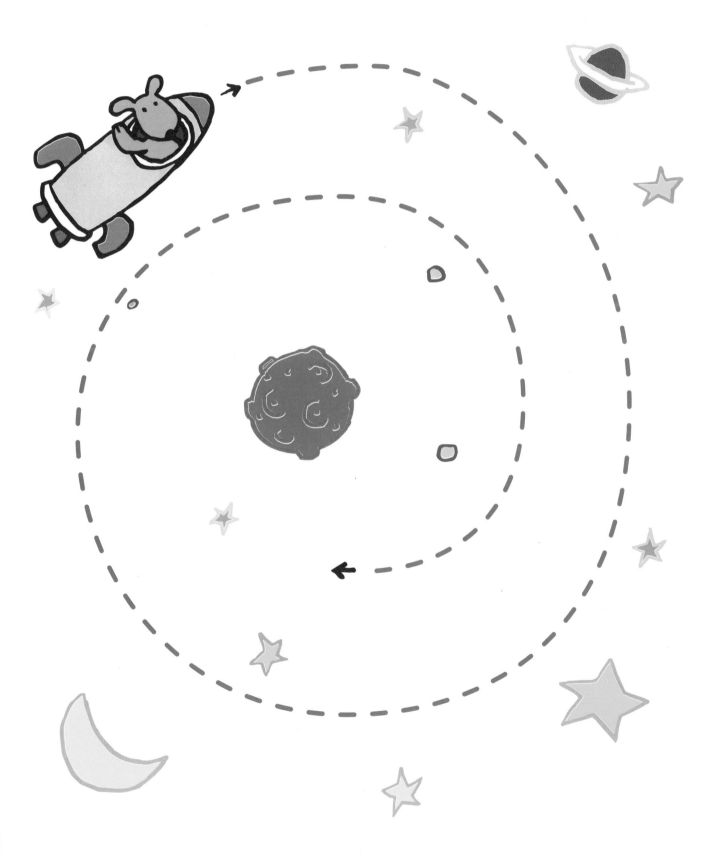

Draw lines in different directions

Show Jack and Jill the way up the hill.

Finish the pattern on the basket.

Show the tired teddy the way up the stairs.

Follow the lines to finish the weather house.

Finish drawing the eggs.

Draw the legs on the little chicks.

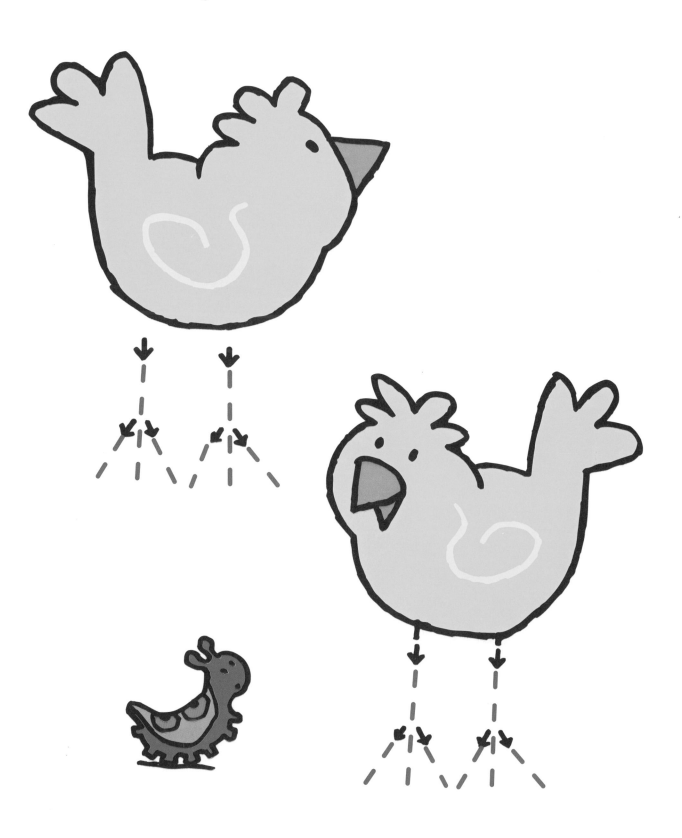

Draw a towel for each teddy to lie on.

Draw the smiley sun in the sky.

Draw the wheels on the tractor.

Finish drawing the snowman and the snow penguin.

Draw diagonal and straight lines

Draw a climbing frame for the monkeys.

Draw a swing and a slide for the rabbits.

Give the little babies lots of curls.

Draw patterns on the slithery snakes.

Draw the scales on the bottom fish to make him look like his friend.

Draw some waves for the whale to swim in.

Finish drawing the castle.

Draw the pattern on the knitting.

To be able to read a particular word, your child
needs to identify the different sounds in that word.

Encourage your child to:

- **point to the first letter in the word;**
- **sound out the letter;**
- **point to the next letter(s);**
- **sound out the letter(s);**
- **then 'blend' the sounds together to say the word.**

Don't let your child struggle too long with a word, quickly offer help rather
than 'waiting' for a reply. Don't hide the pictures – these are visual clues.

Some words can't be read phonetically and are best learnt
as a whole word, for example: the, where, was.
We learn to read these words by familiarity and
remembering them as a whole shape.

Look at each picture and say the word.

apple

bed

cup

dog

Look at each picture and say the word.

egg

fish

In **gate**, the **e** softens the sound of the letter **a**.

fish has three sounds, not four.

gate

horse

Look at each picture and say the word.

insect

jelly

key

log

Look at each picture and say the word.

moon

nest

orange

penguin

Look at each picture and say the word.

queen

ring

In **table**, the **e** softens the sound of the letter **a**.

sun

table

Look at each picture and say the word.

umbrella

vase

window

Look at each picture and say the word.

x

as in box

yo-yo

zebra

Tell a story about the pictures.

One hot day ...

Match the letters to the pictures.

a   f   k   s

Say the sounds.
Ring the pictures that match the sounds.

d		
m		
p		
t		

Colour the picture using the key.

b is for blue.   **r** is for red.
g is for green.   **y** is for yellow.

Colour the pictures.

blue car

green frog

red ball

yellow sun

Ring the same words in each row.

gate

jam   gate   pin

horse

horse   dog   cat

insect

leg   apple   insect

jam

gate   pan   jam

Ring the words that match the pictures.

pen / king

log / cat

moon / cow

nest / bag

Ring the words that match the pictures.

orange
one

pin
pan

queen
quilt

red
rug

Colour the things in the picture that begin with s.

Colour the things in the picture that begin with t.

Look at the pictures. Read the words.
Draw the pictures in the boxes.

a red **u**mbrella

a blue **v**ase   a green **w**indow

Look at the pictures. Read the words.
Draw the pictures in the boxes.

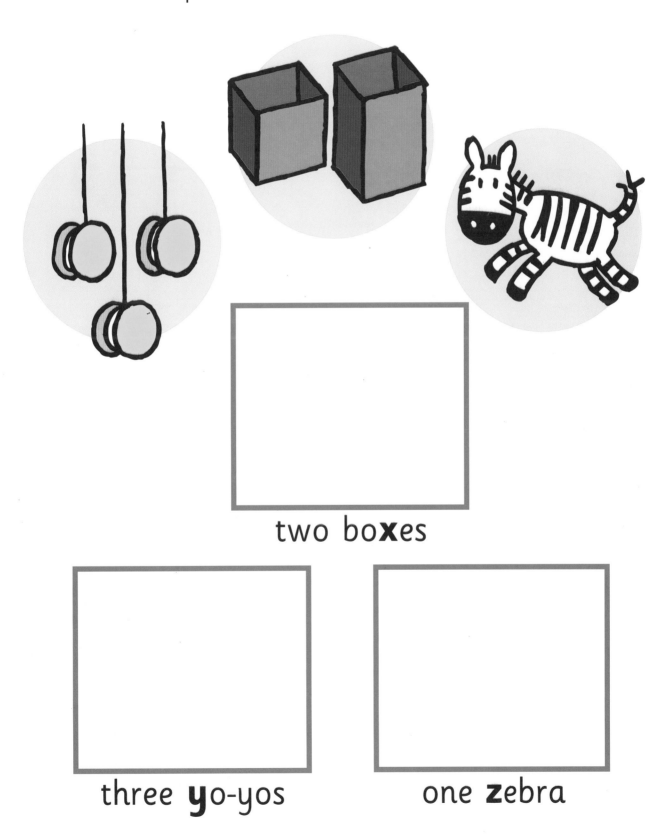

two bo**x**es

three **y**o-yos

one **z**ebra

What do you like best of all?

I like to ...

read ☐

play ☐

dance ☐

draw ☐

Tell a story about the pictures.

One windy day ...

Look at the pictures. Read the words.
Copy the pictures into the boxes.

a dog   a cat

Can you read the words?

A dog and a cat can ...

run

jump

eat

sleep

Read the words.

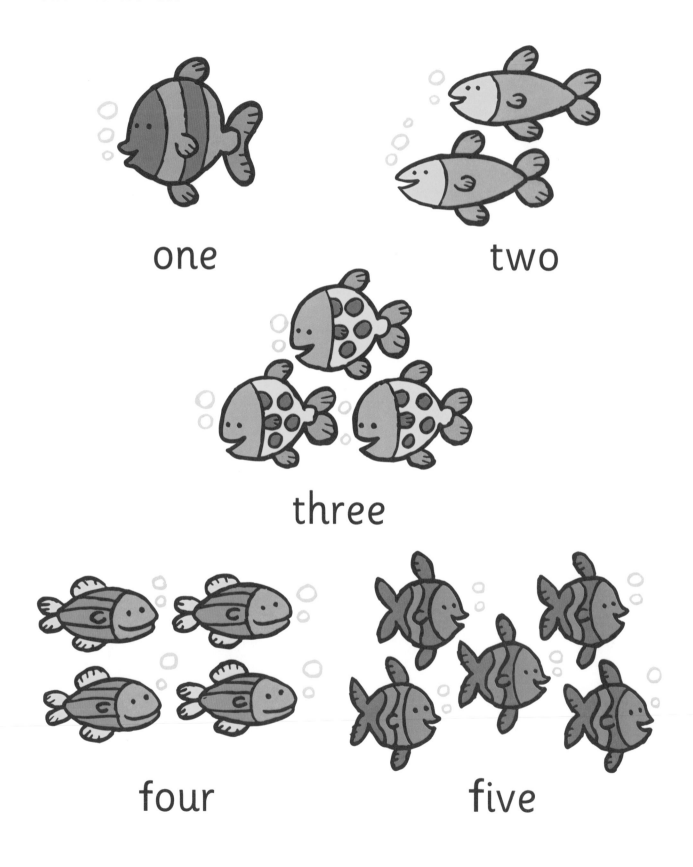

one

two

three

four

five

Say the rhyme.

one   two
three   four   five

once I caught a fish alive

six   seven
eight   nine   ten

then I let it go again!

Tick the picture that comes first.

Tick the picture that comes first.

Join the words that are the same.

mum

dad

boy

baby

girl

mum   dad   boy   girl   baby

Ring the odd one out in each row.

the	the	he	the

in	on	in	in

and	a	and	and

is	it	it	it

dad	dad	dad	day

Read the words.
Draw a picture for each animal.

cow

sheep

horse

pig

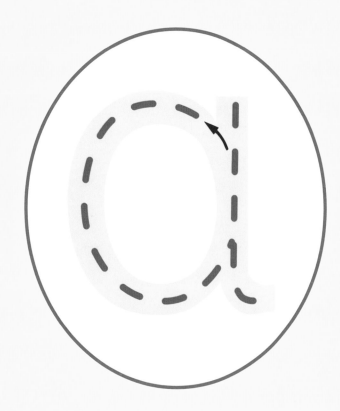

The next pages will show you how to write each letter of the alphabet.
Start at the black arrow and follow the blue dashes. Try to keep inside the blue shadow.

a a a a a a

There are several chances to write each letter because **practice makes perfect!**

Let's go!

It is important that children learn to form the letters correctly, but do remember that writing is a difficult skill for children of this age and you shouldn't worry too much about neatness and correctness at the beginning.

With younger children, you could practise writing letters in a sand tray or "sky writing" (writing letters in the air with a pointed finger).

Children who are left-handed sometimes write letters in a different direction to the ways shown here and this is not a problem as long as their own style is legible and efficient.

Sit at a table to do your best writing!

Write a and b

Follow the ant on the apple to write **a**.

Write **a** on the line.

a a a a a a

Write **b** on the balloons.

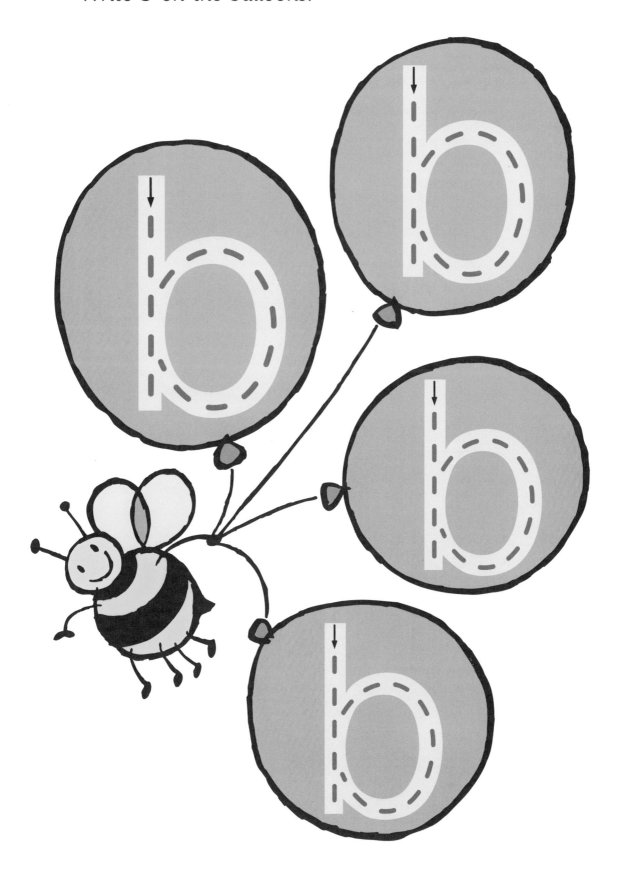

Write c and d

Finish the c pattern on the cups.

Write **d** to finish the dog.

Write **d** on the line.

Write e and f

Write **e** on the egg cups.

Write **f** to finish the fence.

Write **f** on the line.

Write **g** to take the goat through the garden.

Write **g** on the line.

Write **h** to march the men down the hill.

Write **h** on the line.

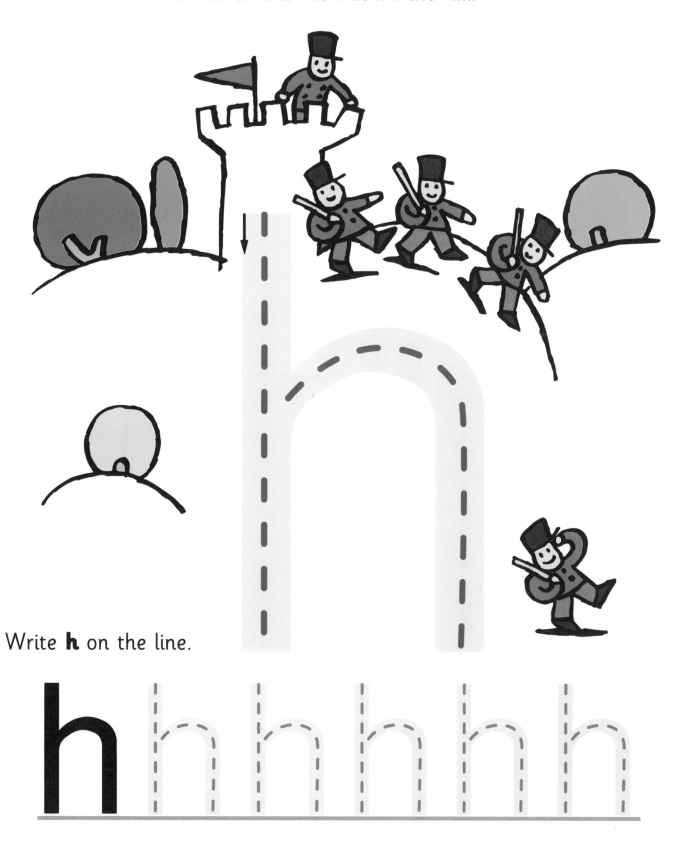

Write **i** to put the icing on the cake.

Write **j** to finish the pattern on the jacket.

Write **k** on the kites.

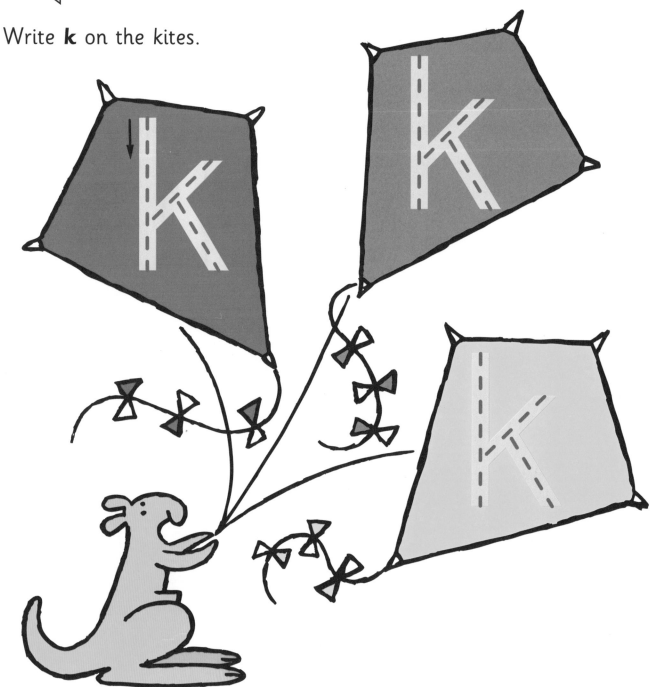

Write **k** on the line.

Write **l** to finish the lorry.

Write **l** on the line.

Write **m** to show the mouse the way to the cheese.

Write **m** on the line.

Write **n** on the beads on Ted's necklace.

Write **o** on the oranges.

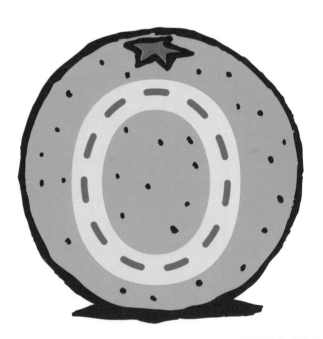

Write **o** on the line.

Write **p** on the peacock.

Write **q** on the pieces of the patchwork quilt.

Write **r** on the rattlesnake to finish the pattern on his skin.

Write **s** to finish the seaweed.

Write **t** on the tortoises.

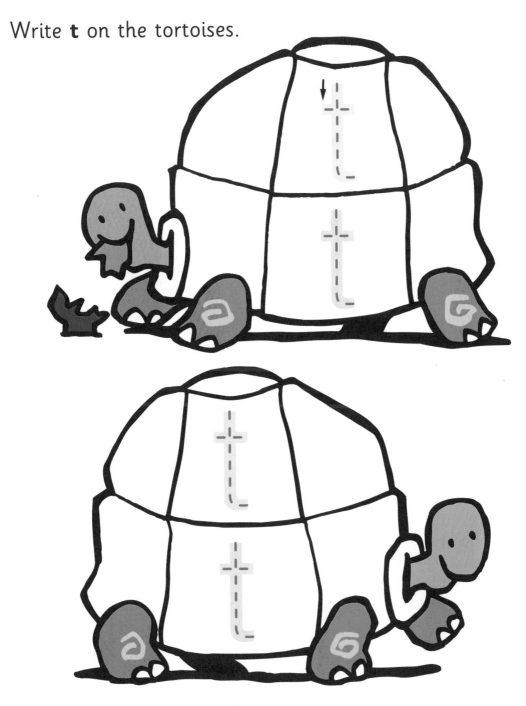

Write **t** on the line.

Write **u** and **v**

Write **u** on the umbrella.

Write **v** to finish the pattern on the vase.

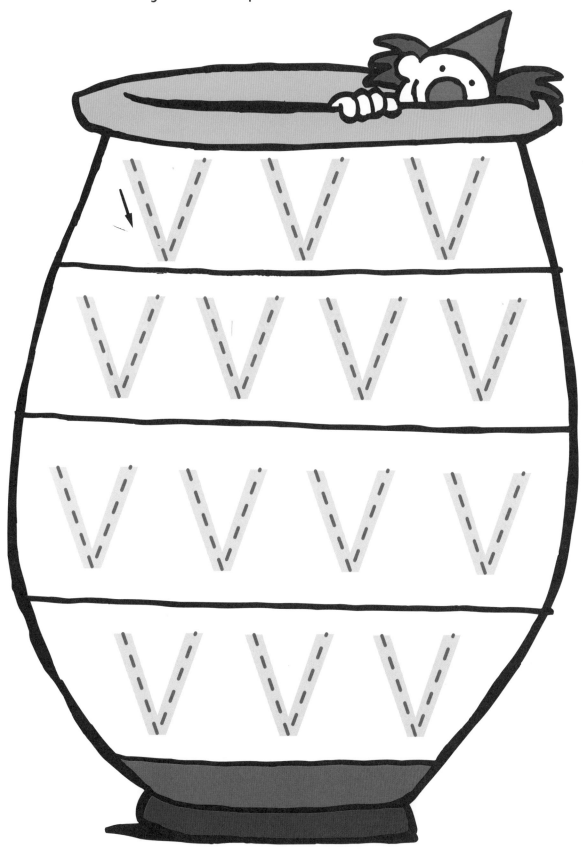

Write **w** on the bricks in the wall.

Write **x** on the card tied to the gift box.

love from

Write **x** on the line.

Write **y** on the yo-yos.

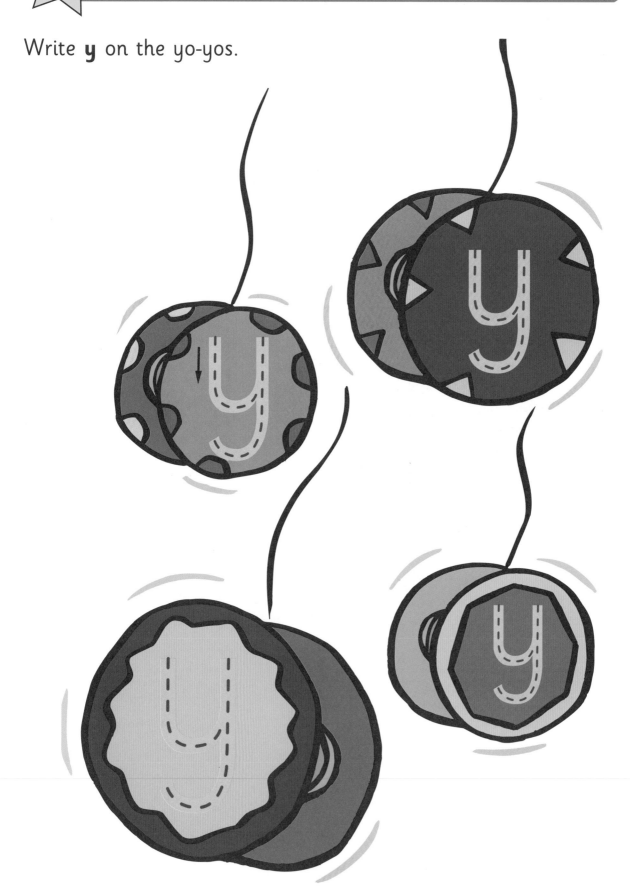

Write **z** to finish the sleepy zebra's coat.

Write **z** on the line.

The clown is juggling letters.
Write the letters in the matching shapes.

Ask a grown-up to write your name on the line below.

Well done, _____ .

Now you can practise writing your name on these lines.

Write the alphabet on the centipede's body.

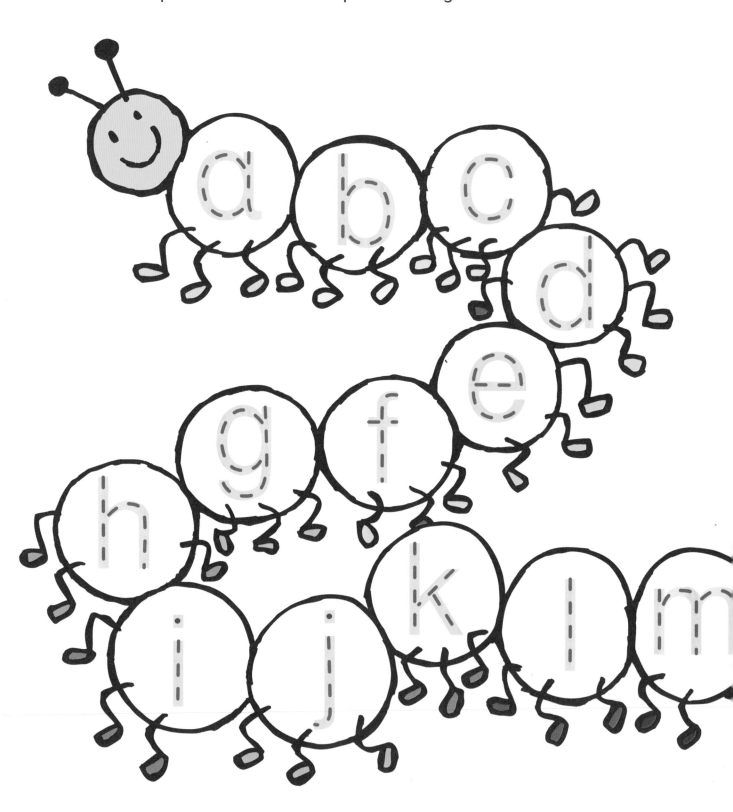

Colour the different letters that appear in your name.

Numbers:
one two three four five

Colours:
blue green red yellow

People:
baby boy dad girl mum

Animals:
cat cow dog duck fish frog horse
insect penguin pig sheep zebra

Other nouns:
apple ball bed book car cup egg
gate jam jelly key king log moon
nest orange pan queen ring rug
sun table umbrella vase window
x as in box yo-yo

Connecting words: a and in is it on the

Tick the boxes to show what you know!
Now I can ...

☐ hold a pencil correctly

☐ **draw straight lines going down**

☐ draw straight lines going up

☐ **draw straight lines going across**

☐ draw curved lines

☐ **draw diagonal lines**

☐ draw circles

☐ **see details in pictures**

☐ tell a story

☐ **say the sounds of all the letters, e.g. for b the letter sound is buh**

☐ say the names of all the letters, e.g. for b the letter name is bee

☐ **match pictures and letters**

☐ identify letter shapes

☐ **see the differences in letter shapes, e.g. b and d, m and n.**

☐ begin to write the letters

☐ **match pictures and words**

☐ read 10 simple words from this book

☐ **read 20 simple words from this book**

Look out for
the companion title:
Mega Maths 3–5

Mega Maths 3–5
ISBN 978 1 4052 4486 2

There are MEGA books for older children, too.
Look out for Maths 5–7
and English 5–7.

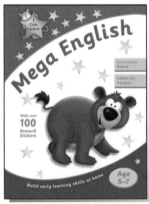

Mega Maths 5–7
ISBN 978 1 4052 4488 6

Mega English 5–7
ISBN 978 1 4052 4487 9

Each book is packed with 128 pages of learning exercises and 100 fun stickers to enjoy.

All titles comply with the National Curriculum (England and Wales) and English and Mathematics 5–14 (Scotland) and are in line with the Curriculum Guidance for the Foundation Stage, and the National Literacy and Numeracy Strategies.

These are the perfect books to help support your child's progress through primary school.